KT-498-489

Contents

Also available from Osborne Books...

Tutorials

Clear, explanatory books written
precisely to the specifications

Wise Guides

Handy pocket-sized study and revision guides

Student Zone

Login to access your free ebooks and
interactive revision crosswords

Download **Osborne Books App** free from the App Store or Google Play Store
to view your ebooks online or offline on your mobile or tablet.

www.osbornebooks.co.uk

Introduction

what this book covers

This book has been written specifically to cover the Unit 'Final Accounts Preparation' which is mandatory for the following qualifications:

AAT Advanced Diploma in Accounting – Level 3

AAT Advanced Certificate in Bookkeeping – Level 3

AAT Advanced Diploma in Accounting at SCQF – Level 6

The book contains a clear text with worked examples and case studies, chapter summaries and key terms to help with revision. Each chapter concludes with a wide range of activities, many in the style of AAT computer based assessments.

Osborne Study and Revision Materials

The materials featured on the previous page are tailored to the needs of students studying this unit and revising for the assessment. They include:

- ■ **Tutorials:** paperback books with practice activities
- ■ **Wise Guides:** pocket-sized spiral bound revision cards
- ■ **Student Zone:** access to Osborne Books online resources
- ■ **Osborne Books App:** Osborne Books ebooks for mobiles and tablets

Visit www.osbornebooks.co.uk for details of study and revision resources and access to online material.

Chapter activities

1 Business organisations

1.1 **(a)** Explain what is meant by the term 'unlimited liability'.

(b) State two types of business organisation where the liability is limited.

(c) State two types of business organisation where the liability is unlimited.

1.2 **(a)** Define a sole trader business.

(b) What are the disadvantages of being in business as a sole trader?

1.3 **(a)** Explain what is meant by the term 'incorporated' for a business organisation.

(b) State two types of business organisation that are incorporated.

1.4 **(a)** What is the governing document for a charity?

(b) What details are contained in the governing document?

(c) Who runs a charity and what are their benefits and liabilities?

1.5 Which of the following businesses have owners with unlimited liability for its debts?

1 Tom Johnson

2 Tom and Tamara Johnson in partnership

3 Tom and Tamara Johnson LLP

(a)	All of them	
(b)	1 only	
(c)	1 and 2	
(d)	2 and 3	

1.6 For a limited company, tick to indicate which of the following statements are true and which are false.

Statement	True	False
Limited companies are unincorporated business organisations		
The Articles of Association set out the written rules about running the company		
The shareholders of a company run it on behalf of the directors		
Companies follow the accounting rules set out in the Companies Act 2006 and in Financial Reporting Standards		
The company's Annual Return, filed at Companies House, is not available for public inspection		

1.7 Where are the main rules governing charities set out?

1 The Charities Act 2011
2 The Companies Act 2006
3 FRS 102 The Financial Reporting Standard applicable in the UK and Ireland

(a)	All of them	
(b)	1 and 2	
(c)	1 and 3	
(d)	2 and 3	

1.8 **(a)** Define a limited liability partnership (LLP).

(b) What is the role of a 'designated member' within an LLP?

2 Framework of accounting

2.1 For the following three primary users of financial statements identify how they might use the information contained in the statements:

User	Use of information
Suppliers	
Customers	
Government agencies	

2.2 Link the boxes with lines to match the uses of financial records and statements with the most likely reason for their use.

Uses	Reason
Internal control	To provide lenders with the current financial position
Measuring business performance	To ensure that financial records are accurate
Obtaining credit/financing	To provide information for tax and other purposes when required to do so
Statutory requirements	To compare financial reports and statements

2.3 Write a brief explanation of the following accounting principles (concepts):

Accounting principle	Explanation
Business entity	
Going concern	
Materiality	

2.4 A business matches income and expenses so that they relate to the same goods or services and the same accounting period.

Of the following accounting principles (concepts), which **one** best describes this rule of accounting?

(a)	Accruals	
(b)	Business entity	
(c)	Going concern	
(d)	Materiality	

2.5 Link each of the boxes on the left with a line to match the fundamental qualitative accounting characteristics that most accurately describes the reason for its use.

Characteristic

Reason

Relevance

Faithful representation

Financial statements can be compared with those from previous years

Financial information is useful to financial users of statements

Users of financial information receive information in time to make decisions

Financial information must correspond to the effect of transactions or events

2.6 The International Financial Reporting Standards Framework for Financial Reporting identifies four supporting qualitative characteristics that make financial information useful.

Under which **one** of the following are users presented with financial information clearly and concisely?

(a)	Timeliness	
(b)	Comparability	
(c)	Verifiability	
(d)	Understandability	

2.7 **(a)** With reference to financial statements, what is the significance of the word 'material' in material misstatements?

(b) Complete the following sentences by filling in the missing word – choose from: overstated, understated, overvalued, undervalued (each word may be used more than once):

(1) If profit is [   ] investors may be encouraged to buy a stake in the business.

(2) If profit is [   ] HM Revenue & Customs will receive a lower amount of tax than should be paid.

(3) If sales turnover is [   ] HM Revenue & Customs will receive a lower amount of VAT than should be paid.

(4) If assets are [   ] a lender may find that security for a loan is less than expected.

2.8 Link the boxes with lines to match the ethical principles with the most likely application of the principles.

Principle   **Application**

| Confidentiality |

| The accountant is not influenced by the owner(s) to manipulate profits |

| Objectivity |

| The accountant is up-to-date with current accounting standards and legal developments |

| Professional competence and due care |

| Financial statements should not contain false or misleading figures or statements |

| Integrity |

| Information from the financial statements is only discussed with those entitled to know |

3 Preparing financial statements

3.1 Cost of sales (cost of goods sold) is calculated as:

(a) Opening inventory + purchases – closing inventory	✓
(b) Purchases – opening inventory + closing inventory	
(c) Opening inventory + purchases + closing inventory	
(d) Purchases – opening inventory – closing inventory	

3.2 Which **one** of the following is used to calculate profit for the year?

(a) Two-column trial balance	
(b) Sales ledger	
(c) Statement of financial position	✓
(d) Statement of profit or loss	

3.3 Which **one** of the following describes net current assets?

(a) The excess of non-current assets over non-current liabilities	
(b) The excess of current assets over non-current liabilities	
(c) The excess of current assets over current liabilities	
(d) The excess of non-current assets over current liabilities	

3.4   **You are to** fill in the missing figures for the following sole trader businesses:

	Sales	Opening inventory	Purchases	Closing inventory	Gross profit	Expenses	Profit/loss* for year
	£	£	£	£	£	£	£
Business A	20,000	5,000	10,000	3,000	....	4,000	....
Business B	35,000	8,000	15,000	5,000	....	....	10,000
Business C	....	6,500	18,750	7,250	18,500	11,750	....
Business D	45,250	9,500	....	10,500	20,750	....	10,950
Business E	71,250	....	49,250	9,100	22,750	24,450	....
Business F	25,650	4,950	13,750	....	11,550	....	–3,450

*Note: a loss is indicated by a minus sign.

3.5 You have the following information about a sole trader business. The value of assets and liabilities as at 1 April 20-1 was:

•	Inventory	£14,270
•	Bank (overdrawn)	£3,210
•	Trade payables	£6,180
•	Non-current assets at carrying amount	£25,500
•	Bank loan	£12,500
•	Trade receivables	£9,450

There were no other assets or liabilities.

(a) Calculate the following as at 1 April 20-1. Do NOT enter any figures as negative.

Assets £

Liabilities £

Capital £

(b) Which of the following best describes goodwill? Tick **one** answer.

(a) A liability, where payment is due in more than one year's time	
(b) An intangible non-current asset which does not have material substance	
(c) A short-term asset which changes regularly	
(d) A tangible non-current asset which has material substance	

3.6   This Activity is about calculating missing balances and the accounting equation.

You are given the following information about a sole trader as at 1 April 20-4:

The value of assets and liabilities was:

- Non-current assets at carrying amount   £35,400
- Inventory   £12,200
- Trade receivables   £21,650
- Bank (overdrawn)   £3,240
- Trade payables   £12,790

There were no other assets or liabilities.

(a)   Calculate the capital account balance as at 1 April 20-4.

£

(b)   On 30 April 20-4, a new machine is purchased for use in the business and is paid for immediately by bank payment. Tick the boxes to show what effect this transaction will have on the balances. You must choose **one** answer for **each** line.

	Debit	Credit	No change
Non-current assets			
Trade receivables			
Trade payables			
Bank			
Capital			

(c)   Which of the following is best described as a non-current liability? Tick **one** answer.

(a) A bank loan repayable in two years' time	
(b) A bank overdraft	✓
(c) Trade payables	
(d) Trade receivables	

3.7   The following trial balance has been extracted by Matt Smith at 31 December 20-4:

	Dr	Cr
	£	£
Opening inventory	14,350	
Purchases	114,472	
Sales revenue		259,688
Rent and rates	13,718	
Heating and lighting	12,540	
Payroll expenses	42,614	
Vehicle expenses	5,817	
Advertising	6,341	
Premises at cost	75,000	
Office equipment at cost	33,000	
Vehicles at cost	21,500	
Sales ledger control	23,854	
Bank	1,235	
Cash	125	
Capital		62,500
Drawings	12,358	
Loan from bank		35,000
Purchases ledger control		14,258
Value Added Tax		5,478
Closing inventory: statement of profit or loss		16,280
Closing inventory: statement of financial position	16,280	
	393,204	393,204

You are to prepare the financial statements of Matt Smith for the year ended 31 December 20-4, using the conventional format.

3.8 An extract from the trial balance of Lisa James is as follows:

Trial balance (extract) as at 31 March 20-7		
	Dr	Cr
	£	£
Opening inventory	17,540	
Sales revenue		127,500
Purchases	77,200	
Sales returns	2,150	
Purchases returns		3,040
Carriage in	680	
Carriage out	1,540	
Discounts received		230
Discounts allowed	470	
Other expenses	35,830	
Closing inventory: statement of profit or loss		19,960

You are to prepare the statement of profit or loss of Lisa James for the year ended 31 March 20-7, using the conventional format.

Incomplete records accounting

4.1   • Cost of sales for the year is £250,000.

   • Mark-up is 50%.

What are sales for the year (net of VAT)?

(a)	£375,000	
(b)	£125,000	
(c)	£250,000	
(d)	£500,000	

4.2   • Sales for the year are £240,000 (including VAT at 20%).

   • Margin is 30%.

   • Opening inventory is £15,000; closing inventory is £20,000.

What are purchases for the year (net of VAT)?

(a)	£260,000	
(b)	£160,000	
(c)	£140,000	
(d)	£145,000	

4.3   You are preparing accounts from incomplete records. Trade payables at the start of the year were £16,400. During the year purchases on credit total £73,400, bank payments to trade payables total £68,100, purchases returns total £1,800, and discounts received total £400.

What is the trade payables figure at the end of the year?

(a)	£13,300	
(b)	£20,300	
(c)	£19,500	
(d)	£23,900	

4.4 Talib Zabbar owns a shop selling children's clothes. He is convinced that one of his employees is stealing goods from the shop. He asks you to calculate from the accounting records the value of inventory stolen. The following information is available for the year ended 31 March 20-2:

- sales for the year, £160,000

- opening inventory at the beginning of the year, £30,500

- purchases for the year, £89,500

- closing inventory at the end of the year, £21,500

- the gross sales margin achieved on all sales is 40 per cent

You are to calculate the value of inventory stolen (if any) during the year ended 31 March 20-2.

Note: VAT is to be ignored on all transactions

4.5 You are working on the accounts of a sole trader business. For the year ended 31 March 20-1 you have the following information:

• Trade payables at 1 April 20-0	£7,240
• Trade payables at 31 March 20-1	£6,180
• Bank payments to trade payables during the year	£51,420
• Cash purchases during the year	£1,730

(a) Calculate the purchases for the year ended 31 March 20-1.

£ ☐

You are now working on the accounts of a different business. This business recently had a fire in its offices and the computer on which the accounting records are kept, together with the majority of the supporting paperwork and computer backups were destroyed.

The business makes all its sales in cash.

You have been asked to produce some figures for the financial statements.

Each source of information below will help find some of the figures that are missing.

(b)   For each source of information indicate the **one** missing figure that it will help to find. Put a tick in the relevant column of the table below.

Note: you do not have sufficient information to find all of the missing figures.

Source of information	Missing figures				
	Total sales	Total purchases	Closing inventory	Profit for the year	Non-current assets
Bank statement					
Physical inventory count					
Gross sales margin					

4.6 This Activity is about finding missing figures in ledger accounts where the records are incomplete.

You are working on the financial statements of a business for the year ended 31 March 20-8. You have the following information:

Day book summaries for the year	Net £	VAT £	Total £
Sales	102,000	20,400	122,400
Purchases	64,000	12,800	76,800
Sales returns	1,800	360	2,160
Purchases returns	1,240	248	1,488

All sales and purchases are on credit terms.

Balances as at:	31 March 20-7 £	31 March 20-8 £
Trade receivables	16,250	18,108
Trade payables	10,380	not known

Further information:	Net £	VAT £	Total £
Administration expenses	22,000	4,400	26,400

Administration expenses are not included in the purchases figure in purchases day book.

Bank summary	Dr £		Cr £
Balance b/d	10,680	Travel expenses	5,290
Sales ledger control	117,950	Administration expenses	26,400
Balance c/d	6,313	Purchases ledger control	72,833
		HMRC for VAT	2,760
		Drawings	10,500
		Payroll expenses	17,160
	134,943		134,943

There were no discounts received on payments made to trade payables.

(a) Find the missing discounts figure by preparing the sales ledger control account for the year ended 31 March 20-8.

Sales ledger control account

(b) Find the closing balance on the purchases ledger control account for the year ended 31 March 20-8.

Purchases ledger control account

(c) Find the closing balance on the VAT control account for the year ended 31 March 20-8.

Note: the business is not charged VAT on its travel expenses.

VAT control account

		Balance b/d	1,470

5 Sole trader financial statements

5.1 A statement of profit or loss shows a profit for the year of £14,900. It is discovered that no allowance has been made for advertising expenses accrued of £620 and rent prepaid of £450 at the year end. What is the adjusted profit for the year?

(a) £14,730	
(b) £15,070	
(c) £15,970	
(d) £13,830	

5.2 Identify whether the following items will be stated in the year end statement of profit or loss as income or expense by putting a tick in the relevant column of the table below.

Item	Income	Expense
Gain on disposal of non-current asset		
Decrease in allowance for doubtful debts		
Irrecoverable debts		
Discounts allowed		
Depreciation charges		
Commission received		

5.3 A statement of profit or loss shows a profit for the year of £18,790. The owner of the business wishes to increase the allowance for doubtful debts by £800 and to write off irrecoverable debts of £250. What is the adjusted profit for the year?

(a)	£18,240	
(b)	£19,840	
(c)	£19,340	
(d)	£17,740	

5.4 You have the following trial balance for a sole trader known as Tysoe Trading. All the necessary year end adjustments have been made.

(a) Prepare a statement of profit or loss (on the next page) for the business for the year ended 31 March 20-6.

Tysoe Trading
Trial balance as at 31 March 20-6

	Dr £	Cr £
Accruals		460
Bank	4,610	
Capital		35,500
Closing inventory	10,200	10,200
Depreciation charges	2,500	
Discounts allowed	490	
Drawings	10,300	
General expenses	25,720	
Office equipment at cost	20,400	
Office equipment: accumulated depreciation		6,500
Opening inventory	11,450	
Payroll expenses	29,610	
Prepayments	990	
Purchases	64,330	
Purchases ledger control		10,310
Rent and rates	7,240	
Sales ledger control	18,920	
Sales revenue		140,680
Value Added Tax		3,110
	206,760	206,760

Tysoe Trading Statement of profit or loss for the year ended 31 March 20-6		
	£	£
Sales revenue		
Cost of sales		
Gross profit		
Less:		
Total expenses		
Profit/loss for the year		

(b) Indicate where accruals of expenses should be shown in the statement of financial position. Tick **one** from:

(a)	As a non-current asset	
(b)	As a current asset	
(c)	As a current liability	
(d)	As an addition to capital	

(c) State the meaning of a credit balance for disposal of a non-current asset in a trial balance. Tick **one** from:

(a)	The business has made a gain on disposal	
(b)	The business has made a loss on disposal	
(c)	The asset has been under depreciated	
(d)	The asset has been part-exchanged on disposal	

5.5 The following adjusted trial balance has been taken from the books of Rhianna Aitken, who sells kitchenware, as at 31 March 20-1:

	Dr	Cr
	£	£
Sales ledger control	4,110	
Allowance for doubtful debts		880
Allowance for doubtful debts: adjustment	220	
Purchases ledger control		11,490
Value Added Tax		1,720
Bank		2,360
Capital		27,500
Sales revenue		166,240
Purchases	85,330	
Opening inventory	18,890	
Shop wages	35,560	
Prepayment of shop wages	440	
Heat and light	2,680	
Rent and rates	10,570	
Accrual of rent and rates		590
Shop fittings at cost	36,000	
Depreciation charges	4,750	
Shop fittings: accumulated depreciation		12,380
Disposal of non-current asset		600
Irrecoverable debts	150	
Drawings	25,060	
Closing inventory	22,450	22,450
	246,210	246,210

You are to prepare the financial statements of Rhianna Aitken for the year ended 31 March 20-1, using the conventional format.

6 Partnership financial statements

6.1 A partnership may choose to over-ride some or all of the accounting rules in the Partnership Act 1890 by the partners entering into a separate:

(a)	Appropriation account	
(b)	Accounting policy	
(c)	Partnership agreement	
(d)	Loan agreement	

6.2 Profits of a two-person partnership are £32,100 before the following are taken into account:

- interest on partners' capital accounts, £1,800
- salary of one partner, £10,000; the other partner does not receive a salary
- interest on partners' drawings, £700

If the remaining profits are shared equally, how much will each partner receive?

(a)	£10,500	
(b)	£11,400	
(c)	£12,300	
(d)	£16,400	

6.3 You have the following information about a partnership business:

> - The financial year ends on 31 March.
> - The partners are Amy, Bob and Caz.
> - Interest on capital is allowed to the partners and is shown in the table below.
> - Interest on drawings is charged to the partners and is shown in the table below.
>
> | | Amy | Bob | Caz |
> |---|---|---|---|
> | | £ | £ | £ |
> | Annual salaries | 10,000 | 12,500 | nil |
> | Capital account balances, 31 March 20-5 | 60,000 | 35,000 | 26,000 |
> | Interest on capital for the year | 3,250 | 1,750 | 1,400 |
> | Drawings for the year | 30,000 | 28,500 | 8,500 |
> | Interest on drawings for the year | 300 | 285 | 85 |
>
> - The profit for distribution to the partners after appropriations is £43,000.
> - Profits are shared in the following percentages: Amy 50%, Bob 30%, Caz 20%.

Prepare the current accounts for the partners for the year ended 31 March 20-6. Show clearly the balances carried down.

- You MUST enter zeros where appropriate.
- Do NOT use brackets, minus signs or dashes.

Select your entries from the following list:

Balance b/d, Balance c/d, Bank, Capital – Amy, Capital – Bob, Capital – Caz, Current – Amy, Current – Bob, Current – Caz, Drawings, Goodwill, Interest on capital, Interest on drawings, Salaries, Share of loss, Share of profit.

Current accounts

	Amy £	Bob £	Caz £		Amy £	Bob £	Caz £
Balance b/d			210	Balance b/d	2,320	830	

6.4 You have the following information about a partnership business:

- The financial year ends on 31 March.
- The partners are Uma, Val and Win.
- Partners' annual salaries:

Uma	£10,400
Val	£15,200
Win	£16,750

  Interest on partner's capital for the year:

Uma	£800
Val	£1,400
Win	£600

- Interest charged on partners' drawings:

Uma	£240
Val	£360
Win	£290

- The partners share the remaining profit of £18,000 as follows:

Uma	30%
Val	50%
Win	20%

- Partners' drawings for the year:

Uma	£14,400
Val	£23,600
Win	£18,200

Prepare the current accounts for the partners for the year ended 31 March 20-4. Show clearly the balances carried down. You MUST enter zeros where appropriate. Do NOT use brackets, minus signs or dashes.

Current accounts

	Uma £	Val £	Win £		Uma £	Val £	Win £
Balance b/d	0	0	300	Balance b/d	1,200	700	0

6.5 This Activity is about preparing a partnership statement of financial position.

You are preparing the statement of financial position for the RS Partnership as at 31 March 20-3. The partners are Ros and Sam.

All the necessary year end adjustments have been made, except for the transfer of profit to the current accounts of the partners.

Before sharing profits the balances of the partners' current accounts are:

- Ros   £500 credit

- Sam   £250 debit

Each partner is entitled to £5,500 profit share.

(a) Calculate the balance of each partner's current account after sharing profits. Indicate whether these balances are DEBIT or CREDIT.

Current account: Ros £	DEBIT / CREDIT
Current account: Sam £	DEBIT / CREDIT

Note: these balances will need to be transferred into the statement of financial position of the partnership which follows.

You have the following trial balance. All the necessary year end adjustments have been made.

(b) Prepare a statement of financial position for the partnership as at 31 March 20-3. You need to use the partners' current account balances that you have just calculated in (a). Do NOT use brackets, minus signs or dashes.

RS Partnership

Trial balance as at 31 March 20-3

	Dr £	Cr £
Accruals		230
Administration expenses	22,680	
Allowance for doubtful debts		670
Allowance for doubtful debts: adjustment		120
Bank	8,910	
Capital account – Ros		30,000
Capital account – Sam		25,000
Cash	490	
Closing inventory	11,670	11,670
Current account – Ros		500
Current account – Sam	250	
Depreciation charges	2,500	
Disposal of non-current asset		300
Office equipment at cost	32,000	
Office equipment: accumulated depreciation		7,900
Opening inventory	10,430	
Purchases	90,850	
Purchases ledger control		13,370
Rent and rates	5,280	
Sales ledger control	37,310	
Sales revenue		130,650
Value Added Tax		1,960
Total	222,370	222,370

RS Partnership
Statement of financial position as at 31 March 20-3

Non-current assets	Cost £	Accumulated depreciation £	Carrying amount £
Current assets			
Current liabilities			
Net current assets			
Net assets			
Financed by:	Ros	Sam	Total

7 Changes in partnerships

7.1 Mia, Nell and Olly are in partnership sharing profits equally. Mia is to retire and it is agreed that goodwill is worth £30,000. After Mia's retirement, Nell and Olly will continue to run the partnership and will share profits equally. What will be the goodwill adjustments to Nell's capital account?

(a)	Debit £10,000; credit £10,000	
(b)	Debit £10,000; credit £15,000	
(c)	Debit £15,000; credit £15,000	
(d)	Debit £15,000; credit £10,000	

7.2 Norman and Oliver are in partnership sharing profits equally. Each has a capital account with a balance of £75,000. Peter joins as a new partner. The profit share will be Norman 40%, Oliver 40% and Peter 20%. An adjustment is made for goodwill on the admission of Peter to the value of £40,000, but no goodwill is to be left in the accounts. What will be the balance of Oliver's capital account after the creation and elimination of goodwill?

(a)	£71,000	
(b)	£79,000	
(c)	£91,000	
(d)	£95,000	

7.3 You have the following information about a partnership business:

- The partners are Sue and Tom.

- The financial year ends on 31 March.

- Uma was admitted to the partnership on 1 April 20-3 when she paid £25,000 into the bank account as her capital.

- Profit share, effective until 31 March 20-3:
  - Sue 60%
  - Tom 40%

- Profit share, effective from 1 April 20-3:
  - Sue 50%
  - Tom 30%
  - Uma 20%

- Goodwill was valued at £30,000 on 31 March 20-3.

- Goodwill is to be introduced into the partners' capital accounts on 31 March and then eliminated on 1 April.

(a) Prepare the goodwill account of the partnership, showing clearly the transactions on the admission of Uma, the new partner.

Goodwill account

(b) Prepare the capital account for Uma, the new partner, showing clearly the balance carried down as at 1 April 20-3.

Capital account – Uma

		Balance b/d	0

(c) Identify whether the following statements about the partnership of Sue, Tom and Uma are true or false by putting a tick in the relevant column of the table below.

Statement	True	False
Sue and Tom have each paid money to Uma when she joined the partnership		
The goodwill of £30,000 is kept in a separate bank account, in accordance with the requirements of the Partnership Act 1890		
Uma has paid a premium for a 20% share of the profits of the partnership		
With goodwill valued at £30,000, Sue and Tom will each have £15,000 extra profit this year		

7.4   You have the following information about a partnership business:

> • The financial year ends on 31 March.
>
> • The partners are Jim, Kit and Leo.
>
> • Interest on partners' capital for the year ended 31 March 20-5:
>
>   – Jim £3,000
>
>   – Kit £2,500
>
>   – Leo £1,500
>
> • Partners' annual salaries for the year ended 31 March 20-5:
>
>   – Jim £20,000
>
>   – Kit £18,000
>
>   – Leo £10,000
>
> • Partners' interest on drawings for the year ended 31 March 20-5:
>
>   – Jim £500
>
>   – Kit £300
>
>   – Leo £200
>
> • Profit share:
>
>   – Jim 50%
>
>   – Kit 30%
>
>   – Leo 20%

Profit for the year ended 31 March 20-5 was £64,000 before appropriations.

Prepare the appropriation account (on the next page) for the partnership for the year ended 31 March 20-5. Use a minus sign for deductions or where there is a loss to be distributed.

Partnership appropriation account for the year ended 31 March 20-5

	£
Profit for appropriation	
Interest on capital:	
Jim	
Kit	
Leo	
Salaries:	
Jim	
Kit	
Leo	
Interest on drawings:	
Jim	
Kit	
Leo	
Residual profit available for distribution	

Share of residual profit or loss	
Jim	
Kit	
Leo	
Total residual profit or loss distributed	

8 Introduction to company financial statements

8.1 Which of the following regulations apply to the preparation of limited company financial statements?

1   IFRSs or FRSs

2   Charities Act 2011

3   Limited Liability Partnership Act 2000

4   Companies Act 2006

(a)	1, 3 and 4	
(b)	1 and 4	
(c)	4 only	
(d)	All of them	

8.2 The directors of Visp Ltd, a recently formed company, seek your guidance on:

(a)   IAS 1 accounting principles (concepts)

(b)   IAS 1 accounting policies

How would you advise them?

8.3   Indicate where the following items will be shown in a company's financial statements.

Item	Statement of profit or loss	Statement of financial position
Revenue		
Tax expense		
Intangible non-current assets		
Tax liabilities		
Share premium		
Dividends paid		
Bank loans		
Finance costs		

8.4   Which of the following statements are **true** for a limited company?

1   The annual financial statements are available for public inspection.

2   The statement of profit or loss must detail every overhead or expense incurred.

3   The year end balance of retained earnings is shown in the statement of financial position as a current asset.

(a) 1 only	
(b) 1 and 2	
(c) 1 and 3	
(d) All of them	

8.5 In a company's statement of financial position, IAS 1 requires that further detail is given – either on the face of the statement or in the notes.

Complete the following table to show the further detail required for the items listed.

Item	Further detail required
Property, plant and equipment	
Trade and other payables	
Inventories	
Issued share capital and reserves	

Answers to chapter activities

1 Business organisations

1.1 **(a)** Unlimited liability means that, should the business become insolvent, the personal assets of the owner(s) may be used to pay the debts of the business.

(b) • limited liability partnerships (LLPs)
• limited companies

(c) • sole traders
• partnerships

1.2 **(a)** A sole trader is an individual in business, trading in his or her name, or under a trading name.

(b) The disadvantages of being in business as a sole trader are:
• the owner has unlimited liability for the debts of the business
• all losses of the business are the owner's responsibility
• expansion is limited because it can only be achieved by the owner ploughing back profits, or by borrowing from a lender
• the owner usually has to work long hours and it may be difficult to find time to take holidays; if the owner should become ill the work of the business will either slow down or stop altogether

1.3 **(a)** Incorporated status for a business organisation means that it is formed into a legal corporation, ie a separate legal body.

(b) • limited liability partnerships (LLPs)
• limited companies

1.4 **(a)** Charities are governed by a trust deed.

(b) The trust deed sets out the name of the charity, its objects and powers, and deals with the appointment of trustees, how meetings are to be run, and the required financial statements.

(c) A charity is run by its trustees, who do not usually benefit personally from the charity but, under certain circumstances, could become liable for the debts of the charity.

1.5 (c) 1 and 2

1.6

Statement	True	False
Limited companies are unincorporated business organisations		✔
The Articles of Association set out the written rules about running the company	✔	
The shareholders of a company run it on behalf of the directors		✔
Companies follow the accounting rules set out in the Companies Act 2006 and in Financial Reporting Standards	✔	
The company's Annual Return, filed at Companies House, is not available for public inspection		✔

1.7   (c) 1 and 3

1.8   **(a)** A limited liability partnership is an incorporated form of partnership, with a separate legal entity, where members are able to limit their personal liability for the debts of the business.

(b) A 'designated member' of an LLP is responsible for ensuring that the legal and accounting requirements are carried out, eg keeping accounting records, arranging for the accounts to be audited if required, preparing and submitting the LLP's Annual Return to Companies House, etc.

2 Framework of accounting

2.1

User	Use of information
Suppliers	• To decide whether to supply goods and services to the business • To assess if the business is able to pay its suppliers
Customers	• To see if the business will be able to continue supplying its goods and services • To assess the ability of the business to provide service in the future, eg spare parts, and to meet warranty liabilities
Government agencies	• To ensure that, if appropriate, the business is registered for VAT • To calculate the tax due – either income tax for sole traders and partnerships or corporation tax for limited companies • To ensure that the charity is being run correctly

2.2

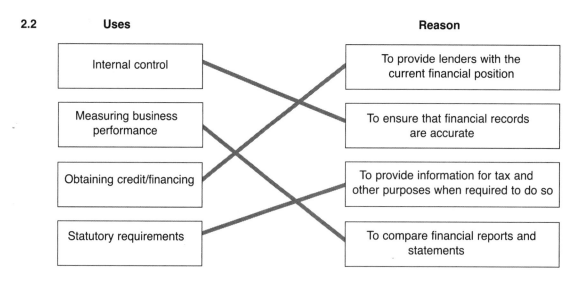

2.3

Accounting principle	Explanation
Business entity	The financial statements record and report on the activities of one particular business
Going concern	The presumption is that the business to which the financial statements relate will continue to trade in the foreseeable future
Materiality	Some items are of such low value that it is not worthwhile recording them separately

2.4   (a)   Accruals

2.5   **Characteristic**   **Reason**

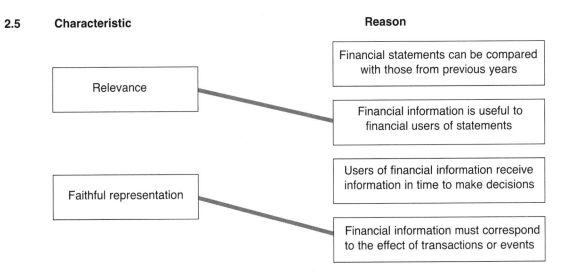

2.6   **(d)**   Understandability

2.7   **(a)**   The use of the word 'material' means that the amount of the misstatement must be significant in relation to the size of the business so as to affect the decisions of users.

   (b)   **(1)**   If profit is **overstated** investors may be encouraged to buy a stake in the business.

   (2)   If profit is **understated** HM Revenue & Customs will receive a lower amount of tax than should be paid.

   (3)   If sales turnover is **understated** HM Revenue & Customs will receive a lower amount of VAT than should be paid.

   (4)   If assets are **overvalued** a lender may find that security for a loan is less than expected.

2.8   Link the boxes with lines to match the ethical principles with the most likely application of the principles.

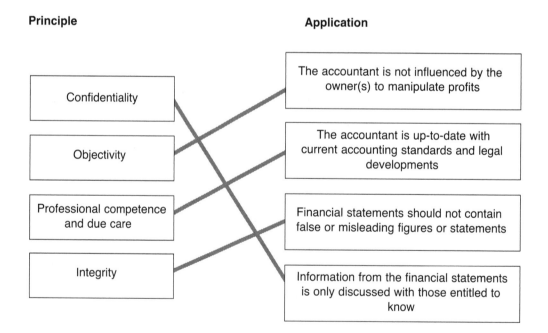

Principle

Application

Principle	Application
Confidentiality	The accountant is not influenced by the owner(s) to manipulate profits
Objectivity	The accountant is up-to-date with current accounting standards and legal developments
Professional competence and due care	Financial statements should not contain false or misleading figures or statements
Integrity	Information from the financial statements is only discussed with those entitled to know

Preparing financial statements

3.1 (a) Opening inventory + purchases – closing inventory

3.2 (d) Statement of profit or loss

3.3 (c) The excess of current assets over current liabilities

3.4 Business A: gross profit £8,000, profit for year £4,000

Business B: gross profit £17,000, expenses £7,000

Business C: sales £36,500, profit for year £6,750

Business D: purchases £25,500, expenses £9,800

Business E: opening inventory £8,350, loss for year £1,700

Business F: closing inventory £4,600, expenses £15,000

3.5 **(a)** Assets: £49,220

Liabilities: £21,890

Capital: £27,330

(b) An intangible non-current asset which does not have material substance

3.6 **(a)** £53,220

(b)

	Debit	Credit	No change
Non-current assets	✔		
Trade receivables			✔
Trade payables			✔
Bank		✔	
Capital			✔

(c) (a) A bank loan repayable in two years' time

3.7

MATT SMITH

STATEMENT OF PROFIT OR LOSS
for the year ended 31 December 20-4

	£	£
Sales revenue		259,688
Opening inventory	14,350	
Purchases	114,472	
Closing inventory	−16,280	
Cost of sales		112,542
Gross profit		147,146
Less:		
Rent and rates	13,718	
Heating and lighting	12,540	
Payroll expenses	42,614	
Vehicle expenses	5,817	
Advertising	6,341	
Total expenses		81,030
Profit/loss for the year		66,116

continued

STATEMENT OF FINANCIAL POSITION as at 31 December 20-4

	£	£	£
Non-current assets			
Premises at cost			75,000
Office equipment at cost			33,000
Vehicles at cost			21,500
			129,500
Current assets			
Inventory (closing)		16,280	
Trade receivables		23,854	
Bank		1,235	
Cash		125	
Total current assets		41,494	
Current liabilities			
Trade payables	14,258		
Value Added Tax	5,478		
Total current liabilities		19,736	
Net current assets			21,758
			151,258
Non-current liabilities			
Loan from bank			35,000
Net assets			116,258
Financed by:			
Capital			
Opening capital			62,500
Add Profit for the year			66,116
			128,616
Less Drawings			12,358
Closing capital			116,258

3.8

LISA JAMES
STATEMENT OF PROFIT OR LOSS
for the year ended 31 March 20-7

	£	£	£
Sales revenue			127,500
Sales returns			–2,150
Net sales revenue			125,350
Opening inventory		17,540	
Purchases	77,200		
Carriage in	680		
Purchases returns	–3,040		
Net purchases		74,840	
		92,380	
Closing inventory		–19,960	
Cost of sales			72,420
Gross profit			52,930
Add: Discounts received			230
			53,160
Less:			
Discounts allowed		470	
Carriage out		1,540	
Other expenses		35,830	
Total expenses			37,840
Profit/loss for the year			15,320

4 Incomplete records accounting

4.1 £375,000

Workings: £250,000 + £125,000 profit

4.2 £145,000

Workings: sales £200,000 net of VAT x 70% = cost of sales £140,000 + closing inventory £20,000 = £160,000 – opening inventory £15,000

4.3 £19,500

Workings: £16,400 + £73,400 – £68,100 – £1,800 – £400

4.4

TALIB ZABBAR CALCULATION OF INVENTORY LOSS FOR THE YEAR ENDED 31 MARCH 20-2		
	£	£
Opening inventory		30,500
Purchases		89,500
Cost of inventory available for sale		120,000
Sales	160,000	
Normal gross sales margin (40%)	–64,000	
Cost of sales		96,000
Estimated closing inventory		24,000
Actual closing inventory		–21,500
Value of inventory loss		2,500

4.5 **(a)** £52,090

Workings: £51,420 – £7,240 + £6,180 + £1,730

(b)

Source of information	Missing figures				
	Total sales	Total purchases	Closing inventory	Profit for year	Non-current assets
Bank statement	✔				
Physical inventory count			✔		
Gross sales margin		✔			

4.6   (a)   Sales ledger control account

Balance b/d	16,250	Sales returns day book	2,160
Sales day book	122,400	Bank	117,950
		Discounts allowed	432
		Balance c/d	18,108
	138,650		138,650

(b)   Purchases ledger control account

Purchases returns day book	1,488	Balance b/d	10,380
Bank	72,833	Purchases day book	76,800
Balance c/d	12,859		
	87,180		87,180

(c)   VAT control account

Purchases day book	12,800	Balance b/d	1,470
Sales returns day book	360	Sales day book	20,400
Administration expenses	4,400	Purchases returns day book	248
Bank	2,760		
Discounts allowed	72		
Balance c/d	1,726		
	22,118		22,118

5 Sole trader financial statements

5.1 (a) £14,730

5.2

Item	Income	Expense
Gain on disposal of non-current asset	✔	
Decrease in allowance for doubtful debts	✔	
Irrecoverable debts		✔
Discounts allowed		✔
Depreciation charges		✔
Commission received	✔	

5.3 (d) £17,740

5.4   **(a)**

Tysoe Trading Statement of profit or loss for the year ended 31 March 20-6		
	£	£
Sales revenue		140,680
Opening inventory	11,450	
Purchases	64,330	
Closing inventory	−10,200	
Cost of sales		65,580
Gross profit		75,100
Less:		
Depreciation charges	2,500	
Discounts allowed	490	
General expenses	25,720	
Payroll expenses	29,610	
Rent and rates	7,240	
Total expenses		65,560
Profit/loss for the year		9,540

(b)   (c)   As a current liability

(c)   (a)   The business has made a gain on disposal

5.5

RHIANNA AITKEN
STATEMENT OF PROFIT OR LOSS
for the year ended 31 March 20-1

	£	£
Sales revenue		166,240
Opening inventory	18,890	
Purchases	85,330	
Closing inventory	−22,450	
Cost of sales		81,770
Gross profit		84,470
Add:		
Disposal of non-current asset		600
		85,070
Less:		
Allowance for doubtful debt: adjustment	220	
Shop wages	35,560	
Heat and light	2,680	
Rent and rates	10,570	
Depreciation charges	4,750	
Irrecoverable debts	150	
Total expenses		53,930
Profit/loss for the year		31,140

STATEMENT OF FINANCIAL POSITION
as at 31 March 20-1

Non-current assets	£ Cost	£ Accumulated depreciation	£ Carrying amount
Shop fittings	36,000	12,380	23,620
Current assets			
Inventory		22,450	
Trade receivables		*3,230	
Prepayments		440	
Total current assets		26,120	
Current liabilities			
Trade payables	11,490		
Value Added Tax	1,720		
Accruals	590		
Bank	2,360		
Total current liabilities		16,160	
Net current assets			9,960
Net assets			33,580
Financed by:			
Capital			
Opening capital			27,500
Add Profit for the year			31,140
			58,640
Less Drawings			25,060
Closing capital			33,580

* sales ledger control £4,110 *minus* allowance for doubtful debts £880

6 Partnership financial statements

6.1 (c) Partnership agreement

6.2 (a) £10,500

6.3

Current accounts

	Amy £	Bob £	Caz £		Amy £	Bob £	Caz £
Balance b/d			210	Balance b/d	2,320	830	
Drawings	30,000	28,500	8,500	Salaries	10,000	12,500	0
Interest on drawings	300	285	85	Interest on capital	3,250	1,750	1,400
Balance c/d	6,770		1,205	Share of profit	21,500	12,900	8,600
				Balance c/d		805	
	37,070	28,785	10,000		37,070	28,785	10,000

6.4

Current accounts

	Uma £	Val £	Win £		Uma £	Val £	Win £
Balance b/d	0	0	300	Balance b/d	1,200	700	0
Drawings	14,400	23,600	18,200	Salaries	10,400	15,200	16,750
Interest on drawings	240	360	290	Interest on capital	800	1,400	600
Balance c/d	3,160	2,340	2,160	Profit share	5,400	9,000	3,600
	17,800	26,300	20,950		17,800	26,300	20,950

6.5 **(a)** Current account: Ros £6,000 CREDIT

Current account: Sam £5,250 CREDIT

(b) **RS Partnership**

Statement of financial position as at 31 March 20-3

	Cost	Accumulated depreciation	Carrying amount
Non-current assets	£	£	£
Office equipment	32,000	7,900	24,100
Current assets			
Inventory		11,670	
Trade receivables		*36,640	
Bank		8,910	
Cash		490	
Total current assets		57,710	
Current liabilities			
Trade payables	13,370		
Value Added Tax	1,960		
Accruals	230		
Total current liabilities		15,560	
Net current assets			42,150
Net assets			66,250

Financed by:	Ros	Sam	Total
Capital accounts	30,000	25,000	55,000
Current accounts	6,000	5,250	11,250
	36,000	30,250	66,250

*sales ledger control £37,310 *minus* allowance for doubtful debts £670

Note: bank £8,910 + cash £490 = cash and cash equivalents £9,400

7 Changes in partnerships

7.1 (b) Debit £15,000; credit £10,000

7.2 (b) £79,000

Workings: £75,000 + (£40,000 x 50%) – (£40,000 x 40%)

7.3 (a) **Goodwill account**

Capital – Sue	18,000	Capital – Sue	15,000
Capital – Tom	12,000	Capital – Tom	9,000
		Capital – Uma	6,000
	30,000		30,000

(b) **Capital account – Uma**

Goodwill	6,000	Balance b/d	0
Balance c/d	19,000	Bank	25,000
	25,000		25,000

(c)

Statement	True	False
Sue and Tom have each paid money to Uma when she joined the partnership		✔
The goodwill of £30,000 is kept in a separate bank account, in accordance with the requirements of the Partnership Act 1890		✔
Uma has paid a premium for a 20% share of the profits of the partnership	✔	
With goodwill valued at £30,000, Sue and Tom will each have £15,000 extra profit this year		✔

7.4 **Partnership appropriation account for the year ended 31 March 20-5**

	£
Profit for appropriation	64,000
Interest on capital:	
Jim	−3,000
Kit	−2,500
Leo	−1,500
Salaries:	
Jim	−20,000
Kit	−18,000
Leo	−10,000
Interest on drawings:	
Jim	500
Kit	300
Leo	200
Residual profit available for distribution	10,000

Note: interest on drawings is *added* to profit (because it is charged to the partners).

Share of residual profit or loss	£
Jim	5,000
Kit	3,000
Leo	2,000
Total residual profit or loss distributed	10,000

8 Introduction to company financial statements

8.1 (b) 1 and 4

8.2 **(a)** IAS 1 requires that companies comply with the following accounting principles (concepts):

- going concern – financial statements are prepared on the basis that the company will continue to operate in the foreseeable future

- accruals – financial statements are prepared on the basis that income and expenses incurred in the same accounting period are matched

- materiality – each material class of similar items is to be shown separately in the financial statements

(b) IAS 1 requires the financial statements of a company should meet the requirements of fair-presentation, including:

- the selection and application of accounting policies to cover specific accounting methods such as inventories, valuation and depreciation of property, plant and equipment.

- the presentation of information so as to provide relevant, reliable, comparable and understandable information.

- where necessary, the provision of additional information to enable users to understand particular transactions.

8.3

Item	Statement of profit or loss	Statement of financial position
Revenue	✔	
Tax expense	✔	
Intangible non-current assets		✔
Tax liabilities		✔
Share premium		✔
Dividends paid	✔	
Bank loans		✔
Finance costs	✔	

8.4 (a) 1 only

8.5

Item	Further detail required
Property, plant and equipment	Shown by different classes – such as property, machinery, motor vehicles, office equipment, etc.
Trade and other payables	Split into amounts owing to trade suppliers, accrual of expenses, etc.
Inventories	If appropriate, sub-classified into raw materials, work-in-progress, finished goods, etc.
Issued share capital and reserves	Shown by classes of shares and reserves.

Practice
assessment 1

This Practice Assessment contains six tasks and you should attempt to complete every task. Each task is independent. You will not need to refer to your answers to previous tasks. Read every task carefully to make sure you understand what is required.

The standard rate of VAT is 20%.

Where the date is relevant, it is given in the task data.
Both minus signs and brackets can be used to indicate negative numbers unless task instructions say otherwise.

You must use a full stop to indicate a decimal point. For example, write 100.57 NOT 100,57 or 100 57
You may use a comma to indicate a number in the thousands, but you don't have to. For example, 10000 and 10,000 are both acceptable.

Task 1

This task is about reconstructing general ledger accounts.

You are working on the accounting records of a sole trader for the year ended 31 March 20-1. The business is VAT registered. You have the following information:

Day book summaries	Goods £	VAT £	Total £
Sales	134,000	26,800	160,800
Sales returns	2,400	480	2,880
Purchases	82,000	16,400	98,400
Purchases returns	1,600	320	1,920

Note: all sales and purchases are on credit terms.

Further information	Net £	VAT £	Total £
Office expenses	20,600	4,120	24,720

Note: office expenses are not included in the purchases day book.

Bank summary	Dr £		Cr £
Balance b/d	10,770	Office expenses	24,720
Trade receivables	152,490	Trade payables	92,845
Balance c/d	3,400	HMRC for VAT	5,245
		Drawings	17,500
		Wages	26,350
	166,660		166,660

Further information:

- Prompt payment discount is recorded using discounts received day book or discounts allowed day book, as appropriate.
- Discounts received during the year were £540, including VAT.
- Discounts allowed during the year were £240, including VAT.

Select your entries from the following list:

Balance b/d, Balance c/d, Bank, Cash purchases, Cash sales, Discounts allowed, Discounts received, Drawings, General ledger, Inventory, Loan, Office expenses, Purchases day book, Purchases returns day book, Rent, Sales day book, Sales returns day book, Value Added Tax, Wages.

(a)   Find the closing balance on the sales ledger control account for the year ended 31 March 20-1.

Sales ledger control account

Balance b/d	18,275	Sales Returns	280
Sales day book	160850	Discount allowed	200
		Bank	133 491

(b) Find the closing balance on the purchases ledger control account for the year ended 31 March 20-1.

Purchases ledger control account

		Balance b/d	10,365

(c) Find the closing balance on the VAT control account for the year ended 31 March 20-1.

VAT control account

		Balance b/d	2,140

Task 2

This task is about incomplete records and applying ethical principles when preparing final accounts.

(a)   Show whether the following is TRUE or FALSE.

Gross sales margin percentage may be calculated as:

$$\frac{\text{Gross profit}}{\text{Cost price}} \quad \text{x} \quad \frac{100}{1}$$

True	
False	✓

You are a trainee accounting technician who prepares final accounts for a number of sole trader clients.

You have the following information about a business for its year ended 31 March 20-5:

- It is not registered for VAT.
- The trader operates with a gross sales margin of 40%.
- Inventory at 1 April 20-4 was £10,500.
- Sales of £77,300 were made.
- Purchases were recorded as £47,930.

77 300 × 60 =
100

(b)   Using this information, complete the following tasks:

(1)   Calculate the cost of sales (cost of goods sold) for the year ended 31 March 20-5.

£ 46380

o/s   10 500
Purch. 47 930
c/s   ? 12 050

(2)   Calculate the value of closing inventory.

£ 12050

46 380 = 10 500 + 47 930 -
46 380 - 58 430 -

p.117

(3) You compare this closing inventory figure with the results of a physical inventory count as at the year end. The total physical inventory value is £500 higher than your calculation.

Which **one** of the following could explain this?

(a) A high value item has not been included in the closing inventory figure	
(b) The trader has made drawings of goods during the year	
(c) Some inventory items have been taken for use in the office	
(d) Some sales returns items have been missed in the count	

(4) Update the value of closing inventory to account for the difference above.

(c) The trader has a policy of allowing customers to settle their accounts three weeks after the sale is made.

Which **one** of the following is most likely to be the total on the sales ledger at the end of the financial year?

(a) £4,400	
(b) £8,900	
(c) £77,300	

(d) As a trainee accounting technician, you are working on the accounts of a car repair business. The owner tells you that she wishes to "show the highest possible profit as I need to impress the bank manager."

How do you respond to this?

(a) It is unethical for an accounting technician to manipulate profit	
(b) A good idea – let's see what we can do to increase profit	
(c) I'll need to tell my supervisor that we are doing this	
(d) I'll do it if, in return, one of your employees can repair my car	

Task 3

This task is about final accounts for sole traders.

You have the following information about events on 1 January 20-1:

- A sole trader started business.
- The business was not registered for VAT.
- The sole trader transferred £15,000 of her own money to the business bank account.
- The sole trader paid £10,000 for a delivery van from the business bank account.
- The sole trader purchased £2,500 of goods for resale; the supplier allowed one month of credit.

(a) Complete the capital account as at 1 January 20-1, showing clearly the balance carried down.

Select your entries from the following list:

Balance b/d, Balance c/d, Bank, Delivery van at cost, Drawings, Purchases, Purchases ledger control, Sales, Sales ledger control, Suspense.

Capital

	£		£

You are now working on the final accounts of another sole trader, Tairo Trading.

You are to prepare the statement of financial position for Tairo Trading as at 31 March 20-1.

- The final trial balance is below.
- A profit of £19,040 has been recorded.
- Tairo Trading has a policy of showing trade receivables net of any allowance for doubtful debts.

(b) Using this information, complete the following tasks:

(1) Calculate the value of trade receivables that will appear in the statement of financial position.

£ 21820

(2) Prepare the statement of financial position for Tairo Trading as at 31 March 20-1.

Do NOT use brackets, minus signs or dashes.

Tairo Trading Trial balance as at 31 March 20-1		
	Dr £	Cr £
Accruals		540
Administration expenses	8,240	
Advertising expenses	3,650	
Allowance for doubtful debts		1,000
Allowance for doubtful debts adjustment		100
Bank		1,270
Capital		30,180
Closing inventory	8,350	8,350
Depreciation charges	6,240	
Discounts allowed	350	
Drawings	11,970	
General expenses	13,860	
Opening inventory	6,290	
Payroll expenses	28,450	
Payroll liabilities		590
Prepayments	330	
Purchases	93,760	
Purchases ledger control		10,260
Rent and rates	10,390	
Sales ledger control	22,820	
Sales returns	900	
Sales revenue		182,720
Value Added Tax		5,640
Vehicles at cost	35,300	
Vehicles accumulated depreciation		10,250
TOTAL	250,900	250,900

Select your entries from the following list:

Accruals, Administration expenses, Advertising expenses, Allowance for doubtful debts, Allowance for doubtful debts adjustment, Bank, Capital, Closing inventory, Depreciation charges, Discounts allowed, Drawings, General expenses, Opening inventory, Payroll expenses, Payroll liabilities, Prepayments, Purchases, Purchases ledger control, Rent and rates, Sales ledger control, Sales returns, Sales revenue, Trade payables, Trade receivables, Value Added Tax, Vehicles accumulated depreciation, Vehicles at cost.

Tairo Trading
Statement of financial position as at 31 March 20-1

	£	£	£
Non-current assets	Cost	Accumulated depreciation	Carrying amount
Current assets			
Total current assets			
Current liabilities			
Total current liabilities			
Net current assets			
Net assets			
Financed by:			
Capital			
Opening capital			
Add profit for the year			
Less Drawings			
Closing capital			

(c) Complete the following:

On 1 April 20-1 capital account has an opening balance of £ _____

debit / credit _____ (delete as appropriate).

Task 4

This task is about the knowledge and understanding underpinning final accounts preparation.

(a) Complete the following:

(1) Which **one** of the list below is a benefit of running a business as an ordinary partnership?

(a) There is limited liability for the debts of the partnership	
(b) The financial statements of the partnership are available to the public	
(c) There is unlimited liability for the debts of the partnership	
(d) With more than one owner there is the possibility of increased capital for the partnership	

(2) A charity uses its resources to fund charitable activities under its control and is run by its

directors / partners / shareholders / trustees (delete as appropriate).

(3) Which of the following organisations make their financial statements available to the public?

1 The Smith Charity

2 Smith and Smith LLP

3 Smith and Smith Ltd

(a) 3 only	
(b) 1 and 2	
(c) 2 and 3	
(d) All of them	

(4) The rules of an ordinary partnership are set out in either the:

Partnership Act / Companies Act / Limited Liability Partnership Act   or in a

written / oral / written or oral   Partnership Agreement (delete as appropriate).

(b)   The International Financial Reporting Standard that sets out the format of final accounts for an organisation adopting IFRS is:

| IAS 1 / IAS 2 / IAS 16 | (delete as appropriate).

(c)   Link the boxes with lines to match the following users of final accounts with the most likely reason for their interest.

User	**Reason**
	Assessment of the contribution of the business to the economy
Suppliers	Decision making relating to their personal investment in the business
The public	Assessment of the ability of the business to supply goods and services in the future
	Decision making relating to provision of goods and services to the business in the future

Task 5

This task is about accounting for partnerships.

(a) Identify whether the following statements about a partnership agreement are true or false by putting a tick in the relevant column of the table below.

Statement	True	False
All partnership agreements state that profits and losses must be shared equally between the partners		✓
A partnership agreement states the salaries to be paid to employees		✓
A partnership agreement may state that interest is to be allowed on partners' capitals	✓	
A partnership agreement may state that interest is to be charged on partners' drawings	✓	

You have the following information about a partnership business:

- Kay, Lee and Matt have been its owners for many years.
- On 31 March 20-1, Kay retired from the partnership. Lee and Matt will continue in partnership. Kay agrees to leave £25,000 of the amount due to her as a loan to the new partnership; the remainder will be paid to her from the partnership bank account.
- Profit share, effective before the retirement:
  - Kay   40%
  - Lee   40%
  - Matt   20%
- Profit share, effective after the retirement:
  - Lee   50%
  - Matt   50%
- Goodwill was valued at £30,000 and has not yet been entered in the accounting records.
- Goodwill is to be introduced into the accounting records on 31 March with the partnership change and then immediately eliminated.

(b) Prepare the capital account for Kay, the partner who is retiring, showing clearly the amount to be paid to her from the partnership bank account as at 31 March 20-1.

Select your entries from the following list:

Balance b/d, Balance c/d, Bank, Capital – Kay, Capital – Lee, Capital – Matt, Current – Kay, Current – Lee, Current – Matt, Drawings, Goodwill, Loan.

Capital account – Kay

	£		£
		Balance b/d	48,500

You have the following information about another partnership business:

- The partners are Jane and Kate.
- The financial year ends on 31 December.
- There is no interest on capital or drawings.

Figures relating to the year ended 31 December 20-1 were as follows:

	Jane	Kate
Profit share	60%	40%
Salary entitlement per month	£1,000	£1,500
Sales commission earned during the year	£8,000	£6,000
Drawings	£22,000 over the year	£1,800 each month

Profit for the year ended 31 December 20-1 was £68,000 before appropriations.

(c) Prepare the appropriation account for the partnership for the year ended 31 December 20-1, and complete the statement below.

You must enter zeros where appropriate in order to obtain full marks.

Use a minus sign for deductions or where there is a loss to be distributed.

Select your entries from the following list.

Drawings – Jane, Drawings – Kate, Salary – Jane, Salary – Kate, Sales commission – Jane, Sales commission – Kate, Share of profit or loss – Jane, Share of profit or loss – Kate.

Partnership appropriation account for the year ended 31 December 20-1

	£
Profit for appropriation	
Residual profit available for distribution	
Share of residual profit or loss	
Total residual profit or loss distributed	

The balance of Jane's partnership current account on 1 January 20-1 was £900 debit. Based on the above transactions and after appropriation of profit for the year ended 31 December 20-1, the opening balance of her current account at 1 January 20-2 will be:

£ [   ]   debit / credit   (delete as appropriate).

Task 6

This task is about final accounts for partnerships and an introduction to reporting regulations for a limited company.

You are preparing the statement of profit or loss for the Beacon Partnership for the year ended 31 March 20-7.

The partners are Yulia and Zoe, who share profits and losses equally. This is their only entitlement to profit.

You have the final trial balance below.

All the necessary year end adjustments have been made, except for the transfer of profit or loss to the current accounts of the partners.

(a) Prepare the statement of profit or loss for the Beacon Partnership for the year ended 31 March 20-7.

If necessary, use a minus sign to indicate ONLY the following:

- the deduction of an account balance used to make up the cost of sales (cost of goods sold)

- a loss for the year

Beacon Partnership
Trial balance as at 31 March 20-7

	Dr £	Cr £
Accruals		690
Administration expenses	20,830	
Allowance for doubtful debts		1,400
Allowance for doubtful debts adjustment	250	
Bank	12,250	
Capital account – Yulia		30,000
Capital account – Zoe		22,000
Cash	240	
Closing inventory	17,380	17,380
Current account – Yulia	950	
Current account – Zoe		790
Depreciation charges	4,650	
Disposal of non-current asset		520
Loan interest paid	760	
Loan payable		5,200
Office equipment at cost	37,100	
Office equipment accumulated depreciation		10,250
Opening inventory	15,140	
Payroll expenses	30,980	
Purchases	85,460	
Purchases ledger control		11,680
Sales ledger control	35,380	
Sales revenue		165,230
Selling expenses	6,340	
VAT		2,570
TOTAL	267,710	267,710

Select your entries from the following list:

Accruals, Administration expenses, Allowance for doubtful debts, Allowance for doubtful debts adjustment, Bank, Capital account – Yulia, Capital account – Zoe, Cash, Closing inventory, Current account – Yulia, Current account – Zoe, Depreciation charges, Disposal of non-current asset, Loan interest paid, Loan payable, Office equipment at cost, Office equipment accumulated depreciation, Opening inventory, Payroll expenses, Purchases, Purchases ledger control, Sales ledger control, Sales revenue, Selling expenses, VAT.

Beacon Partnership Statement of profit or loss for the year ended 31 March 20-7	£	£
Sales revenue		
Cost of sales		
Gross profit		
Add:		
Less:		
Total expenses		
Profit/loss for the year		

(b)   Calculate Yulia's share of profit or loss for the year and her final current account balance. Use a minus sign to indicate ONLY a loss for the year, if necessary.

	£
Yulia – share of profit or loss	
Yulia – final current account balance	

Where will the current account balance for Yulia appear on the statement of financial position for the Beacon Partnership? Choose **one**:

(a)	As a current asset	
(b)	Within the 'Financed by' section	
(c)	Within the 'Current liabilities' section	

(c)   The final accounts for a limited company require more detailed reporting than for a sole trader or partnership.

Which of the following statements are TRUE for a limited company?

1   The statement of profit or loss shows every overhead or expense incurred.
2   The financial statements are available to the public.
3   Finance costs are shown in the statement of profit or loss.

(a)	1 and 2	
(b)	2 and 3	
(c)	1 and 3	
(d)	All of them	

Practice
assessment 2

This Practice Assessment contains six tasks and you should attempt to complete every task.
Each task is independent. You will not need to refer to your answers to previous tasks.
Read every task carefully to make sure you understand what is required.

The standard rate of VAT is 20%.

Where the date is relevant, it is given in the task data.
Both minus signs and brackets can be used to indicate negative numbers unless task instructions say otherwise.

You must use a full stop to indicate a decimal point. For example, write 100.57 NOT 100,57 or 100 57
You may use a comma to indicate a number in the thousands, but you don't have to. For example, 10000 and 10,000 are both acceptable.

Task 1

This task is about reconstructing general ledger accounts.

You are working on the accounting records of a sole trader for the year ended 31 March 20-1. The business is VAT registered. You have the following information:

Day book summaries	Goods £	VAT £	Total £
Sales	154,000	30,800	184,800
Purchases	86,000	17,200	103,200

Note: all sales and purchases are on credit terms. There were no sales and purchases returns during the year.

Further information	Net £	VAT £	Total £
Administration expenses	20,300	4,060	24,360

Notes:

- administration expenses are not included in the purchases day book
- all administration expenses have been paid from the bank during the year

Balances as at:	31 March 20-0 £	31 March 20-1 £
Trade receivables	28,200	29,400
Trade payables	12,600	13,349
VAT (payable)	3,290	4,121

Further information:
- Prompt payment discount is recorded using discounts received day book or discounts allowed day book, as appropriate.
- Discounts allowed during the year were £480, including VAT. *80*
- Discounts received during the year were £306, including VAT. *51*
- Bank receipts from trade receivables during the year were £183,110.
- Payroll expenses paid during the year were £25,490.
- Drawings from the bank during the year were £16,300.
- There were no other bank receipts or payments during the year.

Select your entries from the following list:

Administration expenses, Balance b/d, Balance c/d, Bank, Cash purchases, Cash sales, Discounts allowed, Discounts received, Drawings, Inventory, Payroll expenses, Purchases day book, Purchases ledger control, Purchases returns day book, Sales day book, Sales ledger control, Sales returns day book, Value Added Tax.

(a) Find the missing bank payments figure by preparing the purchases ledger control account for the year ended 31 March 20-1.

Purchases ledger control account

Discount received	306	Balance b/d	12600
Bank	102 145	Purchases	103200
balance c/d	13349		
	115800		115800

(b)   Find the missing bank payment to HMRC for VAT by preparing the VAT control account for the year ended 31 March 20-1.

VAT control account

(c)   Find the closing balance for bank for the year ended 31 March 20-1.

Bank account

		Balance b/d	2,430

Task 2

This task is about incomplete records and applying ethical principles when preparing final accounts.

(a)   Show whether the following is TRUE or FALSE.

Gross profit mark-up percentage may be calculated as:

$$\frac{\text{Gross profit}}{\text{Cost price}} \quad \times \quad \frac{100}{1}$$

True	✓
False	

You are a trainee accounting technician who prepares final accounts for a number of sole trader clients.

You have the following information about a business for its year ended 31 March 20-5:

- It is not registered for VAT.
- The trader operates with a gross profit mark-up of one-half.
- Inventory at 1 April 20-4 was £12,500.
- Inventory at 31 March 20-5 was £15,000.
- Sales of £75,000 were made.

(b)   Using this information, complete the following tasks:

(1)   Calculate the cost of sales (cost of goods sold) for the year ended 31 March 20-5.

£ [   ]

(2)   Calculate the value of purchases for the year ended 31 March 20-5.

£ [   ]

(3)   You compare the closing inventory figure of £15,000 with the results of a physical inventory count as at the year-end. The total physical inventory value is £750 lower than the figure above.

Which **one** of the following could explain this?

(a) A high value item has been included twice in the count	
(b) The trader has made drawings of goods during the year	
(c) A computer bought for use in the office was included in the count	
(d) Some purchases returns items being sent back on 31 March 20-5 have been included in the count	

(4)   Update the value of closing inventory to account for the difference above.

£

(c)   The trader has a policy of allowing customers to settle their accounts one month after the sale is made.

Which **one** of the following is most likely to be the total on the sales ledger at the end of the financial year?

(a) £7,000	
(b) £12,500	
(c) £75,000	

(d)   You are assisting your manager to prepare the financial statements of a client. Unfortunately your manager is to go into hospital shortly and will be away from work for two weeks. She asks you to take on the task of preparing the financial statements.

What should you do? Choose **one:**

(a) Ask your uncle, who is a qualified accountant working for another firm, to help you	
(b) Ask your manager to show you quickly what needs to be done before she goes into hospital	
(c) Ask for another manager to supervise your work	
(d) Tell the client that they will need to find another firm of accountants to prepare the financial statements	

Task 3

This task is about final accounts for sole traders.

You have the following information about a sole trader business for the year ended 31 December 20-1:

- The capital account balance at 1 January 20-1 was £35,600.
- Profit for the year was £16,900.
- Drawings from the bank were £13,300.
- The sole trader took goods for own use of £750.

(a) Complete the capital account for the year ended 31 December 20-1, showing clearly the balance carried down.

Select your entries from the following list:
Balance b/d, Balance c/d, Bank, Drawings, Goods for own use, Profit for the year, Purchases, Purchases ledger control, Sales, Sales ledger control, Suspense.

Capital

	£		£

You are now working on the final accounts of another sole trader, Dracus Trading.

You are to prepare the statement of financial position for Dracus Trading as at 31 March 20-1.

- The final trial balance is below.
- A profit of £16,100 has been recorded.
- Dracus Trading has a policy of showing trade receivables net of any allowance for doubtful debts.

(b) Using this information, complete the following tasks:

(1) Calculate the value of trade receivables that will appear in the statement of financial position.

£ _____

(2) Prepare the statement of financial position for Dracus Trading as at 31 March 20-1.
Do NOT use brackets, minus signs or dashes.

Dracus Trading Trial balance as at 31 March 20-1		
	Dr £	Cr £
Accruals		240
Administration expenses	9,360	
Advertising expenses	2,040	
Allowance for doubtful debts		1,250
Allowance for doubtful debts adjustment		150
Bank		2,480
Capital		39,460
Closing inventory	18,190	18,190
Depreciation charges	7,240	
Discounts received		230
Drawings	15,540	
General expenses	16,780	
Office equipment at cost	30,730	
Office equipment accumulated depreciation		16,250
Opening inventory	17,420	
Payroll expenses	56,890	
Payroll liabilities		550
Prepayments	450	
Purchases	141,080	
Purchases ledger control		15,380
Purchases returns		350
Rent and rates	2,740	
Sales ledger control	33,640	
Sales revenue		250,730
VAT		6,840
TOTAL	352,100	352,100

Select your entries from the following list:

Accruals, Administration expenses, Advertising expenses, Allowance for doubtful debts, Allowance for doubtful debts adjustment, Bank, Capital, Closing inventory, Depreciation charges, Discounts received, Drawings, General expenses, Office equipment at cost, Office equipment accumulated depreciation, Opening inventory, Payroll expenses, Payroll liabilities, Prepayments, Purchases, Purchases ledger control, Purchases returns, Rent and rates, Sales ledger control, Sales revenue, Trade payables, Trade receivables, Value Added Tax.

Dracus Trading
Statement of financial position as at 31 March 20-1

	£	£	£
Non-current assets	Cost	Accumulated depreciation	Carrying amount
Current assets			
Total current assets			
Current liabilities			
Total current liabilities			
Net current assets			
Net assets			
Financed by:			
Capital			
Opening capital			
Add profit for the year			
Less Drawings			
Closing capital			

(c) Complete the following:

On 1 April 20-1 capital account has an opening balance of £ [ ]

[debit / credit] (delete as appropriate).

Task 4

This task is about the knowledge and understanding underpinning final accounts preparation.

(a)   Complete the following:

(1)   Which **one** of the list below is a benefit of an incorporated business?

(a)	There is continuing existence of the business as a separate legal entity	
(b)	The financial statements of the business are available to the public	
(c)	There is unlimited liability for the debts of the business	
(d)	The business is more complex to set up	

(2)   A limited company is run by its:

directors / partners / shareholders / trustees   on behalf of its

directors / partners / shareholders / trustees   (delete as appropriate).

(3)   Which of the following businesses have owners with limited liability for its debts?
1   J Jones, sole trader
2   J Jones and K Jones in partnership
3   Jones and Jones Ltd

(a)	3 only	
(b)	1 and 2	
(c)	2 and 3	
(d)	All of them	

(4)   A charity uses its resources to fund   charitable / profitable   activities and is run by its

directors / partners / shareholders / trustees   in accordance with the

Companies Act / Charities Act / Limited Liability Partnership Act   (delete as appropriate).

(b) With which of the following accounting principles (concepts) does IAS 1, Presentation of Financial Statements, require limited companies to comply?

1   Going concern

2   Accruals

3   Materiality

(a) 1 and 2	
(b) 2 and 3	
(c) 3 only	
(d) All of them	

(c) Link each of the boxes on the left with a line to match the users of final accounts with the most likely reason for their interest.

User   Reason

| Assessment of the security available to cover borrowings |

| Employees |

| Decision making relating to their personal investment in the business |

| Lenders |

| Assessment of the ability of the business to continue to trade in the future |

| Decision making relating to provision of goods and services to the business in the future |

Task 5

This task is about accounting for partnerships.

(a) Identify how the following partnership transactions will be recorded in the accounts – whether capital or current account, and whether debit or credit. Indicate your answer by putting a tick in the relevant column of the table below.

Transaction	Capital account		Current account	
	Dr	Cr	Dr	Cr
Capital introduced		✓		
Partner's salary				✓
Drawings			✓	
Goodwill created		✓		
Share of losses			✓	
Interest on capital				✓

You have the following information about a partnership business:

- The partners are Freya and Gina.
- The financial year ends on 31 March.
- Profit share, effective until 31 March 20-1:
  - Freya 50%
  - Gina 50%
- Profit share, effective after 1 April 20-1:
  - Freya 40%
  - Gina 60%
- Goodwill was valued at £30,000 and has not yet been entered in the accounting records.
- Goodwill is to be introduced into the accounting records on 31 March with the partnership change and then immediately eliminated.

(b)   Prepare the partners' capital accounts to record the change in profit share, showing clearly the balance carried down.

Select your entries from the following list:

Balance b/d, Balance c/d, Bank, Capital – Freya, Capital – Gina, Current – Freya, Current – Gina, Drawings, Goodwill.

Partners' capital accounts

	Freya £	Gina £		Freya £	Gina £
			Balances b/d	24,000	36,000

You have the following information about another partnership business:

- The partners are Rob and Sue.
- The financial year ends on 31 December.
- There is no interest on capital or drawings.

Figures relating to the year ended 31 December 20-1 were as follows:

	Rob	Sue
Profit share	40%	60%
Salary entitlement per month	£900	£1,150
Sales commission earned during the year	£4,500	£5,750
Drawings	£1,350 each month	£18,000 over the year

Profit for the year ended 31 December 20-1 was £33,000 before appropriations.

(c) Prepare the appropriation account for the partnership for the year ended 31 December 20-1, and complete the statement below.

You must enter zeros where appropriate in order to obtain full marks.

Use a minus sign for deductions or where there is a loss to be distributed.

Select your entries from the following list.

Drawings – Rob, Drawings – Sue, Salary – Rob, Salary – Sue, Sales commission – Rob, Sales commission – Sue, Share of profit or loss – Rob, Share of profit or loss – Sue.

Partnership appropriation account for the year ended 31 December 20-1

	£
Profit for appropriation	.
Residual profit available for distribution	
Share of residual profit or loss	
Total residual profit or loss distributed	

The balance of Rob's partnership current account on 1 January 20-1 was £650 credit. Based on the above transactions and after appropriation of profit for the year ended 31 December 20-1, the opening balance of his current account at 1 January 20-2 will be:

£ _____ debit / credit (delete as appropriate).

Task 6

This task is about final accounts for partnerships and an introduction to reporting regulations for a limited company.

You are preparing the statement of profit or loss for the Sarton Partnership for the year ended 31 March 20-1.

The partners are Sara and Toni, who share profits and losses in the following percentages: Sara 60% and Toni 40%. This is their only entitlement to profit.

You have the final trial balance below.

All the necessary year end adjustments have been made, except for the transfer of profit or loss to the current accounts of the partners.

(a) Prepare the statement of profit or loss for the Sarton Partnership for the year ended 31 March 20-1.

If necessary, use a minus sign to indicate ONLY the following:

- the deduction of an account balance used to make up the cost of sales (cost of goods sold)

- a loss for the year

Sarton Partnership
Trial balance as at 31 March 20-1

	Dr £	Cr £
Accruals		400
Administration expenses	16,210	
Allowance for doubtful debts		830
Allowance for doubtful debts adjustment	120	
Bank	15,330	
Capital account – Sara		15,000
Capital account – Toni		12,500
Cash	180	
Closing inventory	6,090	6,090
Current account – Sara		2,620
Current account – Toni	460	
Depreciation charges	4,750	
Disposal of non-current asset		160
Loan interest paid	1,095	
Loan payable		24,400
Machinery at cost	29,770	
Machinery accumulated depreciation		12,800
Opening inventory	5,150	
Payroll expenses	24,975	
Purchases	45,930	
Purchases ledger control		6,420
Sales ledger control	15,360	
Sales revenue		95,320
Selling expenses	12,410	
VAT		1,290
TOTAL	177,830	177,830

Select your entries from the following list:

Accruals, Administration expenses, Allowance for doubtful debts, Allowance for doubtful debts adjustment, Bank, Capital account – Sara, Capital account – Toni, Cash, Closing inventory, Current account – Sara, Current account – Toni, Depreciation charges, Disposal of non-current asset, Loan interest paid, Loan payable, Machinery at cost, Machinery accumulated depreciation, Opening inventory, Payroll expenses, Purchases, Purchases ledger control, Sales ledger control, Sales revenue, Selling expenses, VAT.

Sarton Partnership Statement of profit or loss for the year ended 31 March 20-1	£	£
Sales revenue		
Cost of sales		
Gross profit		
Add:		
Less:		
Total expenses		
Profit/loss for the year		

(b) Calculate Sara's share of profit or loss for the year and her final current account balance. Use a minus sign to indicate ONLY a loss for the year, if necessary.

	£
Sara – share of profit or loss	
Sara – final current account balance	

How will the current account balance for Sara appear on the statement of financial position for the Sarton Partnership? Choose **one**:

(a)	Deducted within the 'Financed by' section	
(b)	Added within the 'Financed by' section	
(c)	Added within the 'Current liabilities' section	

(c) Show where the following items will appear in a limited company's financial statements:

Item	Statement of profit or loss	Statement of financial position
Property, plant and equipment		
Tax expense		
Finance costs		
Share premium		

Practice assessment 3

This Practice Assessment contains six tasks and you should attempt to complete every task. Each task is independent. You will not need to refer to your answers to previous tasks. Read every task carefully to make sure you understand what is required.

The standard rate of VAT is 20%.

Where the date is relevant, it is given in the task data.
Both minus signs and brackets can be used to indicate negative numbers unless task instructions say otherwise.

You must use a full stop to indicate a decimal point. For example, write 100.57 NOT 100,57 or 100 57
You may use a comma to indicate a number in the thousands, but you don't have to. For example, 10000 and 10,000 are both acceptable.

Task 1

This task is about reconstructing general ledger accounts.

You are working on the accounting records of a sole trader for the year ended 31 March 20-6.

The business is not registered for VAT.

You have the following information:

Receipts and payments recorded in the bank account include:

	£
Amounts from credit customers	67,031
Amounts to credit suppliers	27,846
Drawings	12,500
Office expenses	19,361
Bank interest paid	247

Balance at:	31 March 20-5	31 March 20-6
	£	£
Trade receivables	8,216	9,047
Trade payables	4,367	4,498
Closing inventory	4,221	4,864
Bank	3,219 credit	1,246 debit

You are also told that:

• All sales are on credit terms.

• Sales totalled £68,422 for the year.

Select your entries from the following list:

Allowance for doubtful debts, Allowance for doubtful debts adjustment, Balance b/d, Balance c/d, Bank, Bank interest paid, Capital, Cash purchases, Cash sales, Closing inventory, Credit purchases, Credit sales, Drawings, Irrecoverable debts, Office expenses, Opening inventory, Purchases ledger control, Sales ledger control.

(a) Find the credit purchases figure by preparing the purchases ledger control account for the year ended 31 March 20-6.

Purchases ledger control account

bal c/d	4498	bal b/d	4367

During the year, a customer was declared bankrupt. The amount has been written off in full.

(b) Find the amount written off by preparing the sales ledger control account for the year ended 31 March 20-6.

Sales ledger control account

(c) Find the cash purchases by preparing a summarised bank account for the year ended 31 March 20-6.

Bank account

Task 2

This task is about incomplete records and applying ethical principles when preparing final accounts.

(a)   Show whether the following is TRUE or FALSE.

Gross sales margin percentage may be calculated as:

$$\frac{\text{Gross profit}}{\text{Purchases}} \quad \text{x} \quad \frac{100}{1}$$

True	
False	✓

You are a trainee accounting technician who prepares final accounts for a number of sole trader clients.

You have the following information about a business for its year ended 31 March 20-5:

- It is not registered for VAT.
- The trader operates with a gross sales margin of one-fifth.
- Sales of £80,000 were made.
- Inventory at 1 April 20-4 was £7,000.
- Inventory at 31 March 20-5 was £10,000.

(b)   Using this information, complete the following tasks.

(1)   Calculate the cost of sales (cost of goods sold) for the year ended 31 March 20-5.

£ [　　　　　　　]

(2)   Calculate the purchases for the year ended 31 March 20-5.

£ [　　　　　　　]

(3) You compare the closing inventory figure of £10,000, with the results of a physical inventory count as at the year end. The total physical inventory value is £200 higher than the figure above.

Which **one** of the following could explain this?

(a) A high value item has been missed in the count	
(b) The trader has made drawings of goods during the year	
(c) Some inventory items have been taken for use in the office	
(d) Some sales returns items have been included twice in the count	-

(4) Update the value of closing inventory to account for the difference above.

£

(c) The trader has a policy of allowing customers to settle their accounts six weeks after the sale is made.

Which **one** of the following is most likely to be the total on the sales ledger at the end of the financial year?

(a) £7,000	
(b) £9,300	
(c) £80,000	

(d) Which **one** of these is an example of an accountant applying the ethical principle of integrity?

(a) The accountant is up-to-date with current accounting standards and legal developments	
(b) The financial statements prepared by the accountant do not contain false or misleading figures and statements	
(c) The accountant records all aspects of the preparation of financial statements in an honest and truthful way	
(d) The content of the financial statements prepared by the accountant is not discussed with family and friends	

Task 3

This task is about final accounts for sole traders.

You have the following information about events on 1 April 20-5:

• A sole trader started business.

• The business was not registered for VAT.

• The sole trader transferred £20,000 of her own money to the business bank account.

• The sole trader paid £8,000 for a delivery van from the business bank account.

• The sole trader purchased £3,500 of goods for resale, using the trader's personal bank account.

(a) Complete the capital account as at 1 April 20-5, showing clearly the balance carried down.

Select your entries from the following list:
Balance b/d, Balance c/d, Bank, Delivery van at cost, Drawings, Purchases, Purchases ledger control, Sales, Sales ledger control, Suspense.

Capital

	£		£

You are now working on the final accounts of another sole trader, Hanslo Trading.

You are to prepare the statement of profit or loss for Hanslo Trading for the year ended 31 March 20-6.

• The final trial balance is below.

• Hanslo Trading has the following accounting policies:

    – sales revenue includes sales returns, if any

    – purchases includes purchases returns and carriage inwards, if any.

(b) Using this information, complete the following tasks:

(1) Calculate the sales revenue figure to be included in the statement of profit or loss for Hanslo Trading.

£ [   ]

(2) Calculate the purchases figure to be included in the statement of profit or loss for Hanslo Trading.

£

(3) Prepare a statement of profit or loss for Hanslo Trading for the year ended 31 March 20-6. If necessary, use a minus sign to indicate ONLY the following:

- the deduction of an account balance used to make up cost of sales (cost of goods sold)
- a loss for the year

Hanslo Trading
Trial balance as at 31 March 20-6

	Dr £	Cr £
Accruals		740
Bank	4,850	
Capital		65,000
Carriage inwards	1,430	
Carriage outwards	2,790	
Cash	220	
Closing inventory	11,340	11,340
Depreciation charges	4,520	
Disposal of non-current assets		990
Drawings	16,500	
General expenses	23,920	
Opening inventory	9,760	
Payroll expenses	49,050	
Prepayments	1,310	
Purchases	47,860	
Purchases ledger control		7,530
Sales ledger control	18,170	
Sales returns	2,160	
Sales revenue		125,860
Value Added Tax		2,710
Vehicles at cost	35,000	
Vehicles accumulated depreciation		14,710
Total	228,880	228,880

Select your entries from the following list:

Accruals, Bank, Capital, Carriage inwards, Carriage outwards, Cash, Closing inventory, Depreciation charges, Disposal of non-current assets, Drawings, General expenses, Opening inventory, Payroll expenses, Prepayments, Purchases, Purchases ledger control, Sales ledger control, Sales returns, Sales revenue, Value Added Tax, Vehicles at cost, Vehicles accumulated depreciation.

Hanslo Trading
Statement of profit or loss for the year ended 31 March 20-6

	£	£
Sales revenue		
Cost of sales		
Gross profit		
Add:		
Less:		
Total expenses		
Profit/loss for the year		

(c)   Identify the meaning of a debit balance for disposal of non-current assets in a trial balance. Tick **one** from:

(a)	The business has made a gain on disposal	
(b)	The business has made a loss on disposal	
(c)	The asset has been over-depreciated	
(d)	The asset has been part-exchanged on disposal	

Task 4

This task is about the knowledge and understanding underpinning final accounts preparation.

(a)   Complete the following:

(1)   Which **one** of the list below best describes material misstatement?

(a)	When the accountant preparing the financial statements allows the influence of others to bias or override professional judgements	
(b)	When users of financial statements do not receive information in time to make economic decisions	
(c)	When the accounting principle of materiality has not been applied	
(d)	When information contained in the financial statements is untrue and could influence the economic decisions of users	

(2)   The governing document of a charity is the:

Articles of Association / Members' Agreement / Trust Deed   (delete as appropriate).

(3)   Which of the following organisations have incorporated status?

1   The Clark Charity
2   Clark and Clark LLP
3   Clark and Clark Ltd

(a)	3 only	
(b)	1 and 2	
(c)	2 and 3	
(d)	All of them	

(4)   A company incorporates by registering under:

IAS 1 / the Companies Act / the Articles of Association   (delete as appropriate).

Once registered, a company is run by its:

shareholders / directors / trustees   (delete as appropriate).

(b) In order for financial information to be useful, a business selects its accounting policies to fit in with the two fundamental qualitative accounting characteristics.

From the following list tick the **two** fundamental qualitative accounting characteristics:

(a)	Relevance	
(b)	Timeliness	
(c)	Verifiability	
(d)	Faithful representation	

(c) Link each of the boxes on the left with a line to match the users of final accounts with the most likely reason for their interest.

User

Reason

Assessment of the contribution of the business to the economy

Existing shareholders

Decision making relating to their personal investment in the business

Customers

Assessment of the ability of the business to supply goods and services in the future

Decision making relating to provision of goods and services to the business in the future

Task 5

This task is about accounting for partnerships.

(a) Identify whether the following statements about partnerships are true or false by putting a tick in the relevant column of the table below.

Statement	True	False
When a new partner is admitted to a partnership business, existing partners pay a premium to welcome the new partner		✓
When a partner retires from a partnership business, the balance of his or her capital and current accounts is due to the partner from the partnership	✓	
Goodwill is kept in a separate bank account in accordance with the requirements of the Partnership Act 1890		✓

You have the following information about a partnership business:

- Hal and Ian have been the owners of a partnership business for many years sharing profits and losses in the ratio 2:1, with Hal receiving the larger share.
- On 1 April 20-5, the partnership agreement was changed so that Hal and Ian will share profits and losses in the ratio 3:2, with Hal receiving the larger share.
- Goodwill was valued at £60,000 at this date and has already been introduced into the partnership accounting records. It now needs to be eliminated.

(b) (1) Show the entries required to eliminate the goodwill from the partnership accounting records on 1 April 20-5.

Select your entries for the 'Account name' column from the following list:

Balance b/d, Balance c/d, Bank, Capital – Hal, Capital – Ian, Current – Hal, Current – Ian, Goodwill.

Account name	Amount £	Debit	Credit

(2)   Complete the following statements regarding Hal's position in the partnership at the end of the day on 1 April 20-5.

Hal's share of the profits and losses in the partnership has:

| increased / decreased / stayed the same | after the change in the partnership agreement.

(Delete as appropriate).

Hal's capital account balance has:

| increased / decreased / stayed the same | after the change in the partnership agreement.

(Delete as appropriate).

You have the following information about another partnership business:

- The partners are Amy and Bob.
- The financial year ends on 31 December.
- There is no interest on drawings.

Figures relating to the year ended 31 December 20-1 were as follows:

	Amy	Bob
Profit share	70%	30%
Salary entitlement per month	£1,200	£1,800
Interest on capital for the year	£3,250	£1,750
Drawings	£28,000 over the year	£2,000 each month

Profit for the year ended 31 December 20-1 was £53,000 before appropriations.

(c)   Prepare the appropriation account for the partnership for the year ended 31 December 20-1, and complete the statement below.

You must enter zeros where appropriate in order to obtain full marks.

Use a minus sign for deductions or where there is a loss to be distributed.

Select your entries from the following list.

Drawings – Amy, Drawings – Bob, Interest on capital – Amy, Interest on capital – Bob, Salary – Amy, Salary – Bob, Share of profit or loss – Amy, Share of profit or loss – Bob.

Partnership appropriation account for the year ended 31 December 20-1

	£
Profit for appropriation	
Residual profit available for distribution	
Share of residual profit or loss	
Total residual profit or loss distributed	

The balance of Amy's partnership current account on 1 January 20-1 was £850 credit. Based on the above transactions and after appropriation of profit for the year ended 31 December 20-1, the opening balance of her current account at 1 January 20-2 will be:

£ [   ]   debit / credit   (delete as appropriate).

Task 6

This task is about preparing a partnership statement of financial position.

You are preparing the statement of financial position for the Blenheim Partnership as at 31 March 20-6.

The partners are Yan and Zeb, who share profits and losses in the ratio 2:3, with Zeb taking the larger share. This is their only entitlement to profit.

You have the final trial balance on the next page.

All the necessary year end adjustments have been made, except for the transfer of £36,000 profit to the current accounts of the partners.

(a) Calculate the balance of each partner's current account after sharing profits. Indicate whether these balances are DEBIT or CREDIT (delete as appropriate).

Current account: Yan £	DEBIT / CREDIT
Current account: Zeb £	DEBIT / CREDIT

(b) Prepare a statement of financial position for the partnership as at 31 March 20-6. You need to use the partners' current account balances that you have just calculated in (a).

Do NOT use brackets, minus signs or dashes.

(c) Preparation of the final accounts for a limited company at its year end requires more detailed reporting than for a sole trader or partnership.

Which of the following statements are TRUE for a limited company?

1   IAS 1 sets out a required format for statements of financial position.

2   The Companies Act requires company directors to keep adequate accounting records.

3   IAS 1 requires companies to comply with the accounting principles (concepts) of going concern, accruals, and materiality.

(a)	1 and 2	
(b)	2 and 3	
(c)	1 and 3	
(d)	All of them	

Blenheim Partnership
Trial balance as at 31 March 20-6

	Dr £	Cr £
Accruals		550
Administration expenses	39,179	
Bank	11,355	
Capital account – Yan		35,000
Capital account – Zeb		50,000
Closing inventory	17,830	17,830
Current account – Yan	820	
Current account – Zeb		2,090
Depreciation charges	5,400	
Discounts received		1,210
Disposal of non-current asset	455	
Irrecoverable debts	394	
Machinery at cost	87,500	
Machinery accumulated depreciation		22,840
Opening inventory	16,380	
Payroll expenses	33,865	
Payroll liabilities		240
Prepayments	725	
Purchases	261,340	
Purchases ledger control		33,025
Sales ledger control	64,055	
Sales returns	2,390	
Sales revenue		390,860
Travel expenses	14,497	
Value Added Tax		2,540
Total	556,185	556,185

Select your entries from the following list:

Accruals, Administration expenses, Bank, Capital account – Yan, Capital account – Zeb, Closing inventory, Current account – Yan, Current account – Zeb, Depreciation charges, Discounts received, Disposal of non-current asset, Irrecoverable debts, Machinery at cost, Machinery accumulated depreciation, Opening inventory, Payroll expenses, Payroll liabilities, Prepayments, Purchases, Purchases ledger control, Sales ledger control, Sales returns, Sales revenue, Trade payables, Trade receivables, Travel expenses, Value Added Tax.

Blenheim Partnership
Statement of financial position as at 31 March 20-6

	£	£	£
Non-current assets	Cost	Accumulated depreciation	Carrying amount
Current assets			
Total current assets			
Current liabilities			
Total current liabilities			
Net current assets			
Net assets			
Financed by:	Yan	Zeb	Total

Answers to practice assessment 1

Task 1

(a)   **Sales ledger control account**

Balance b/d	18,275	Sales returns day book	2,880
Sales day book	160,800	Bank	152,490
		Discounts allowed	240
		Balance c/d	23,465
	179,075		179,075

(b)   **Purchases ledger control account**

Purchases returns day book	1,920	Balance b/d	10,365
Bank	92,845	Purchases day book	98,400
Discounts received	540		
Balance c/d	13,460		
	108,765		108,765

(c)   **VAT control account**

Sales returns day book	480	Balance b/d	2,140
Purchases day book	16,400	Sales day book	26,800
Discounts allowed	40	Purchases returns day book	320
Office expenses	4,120	Discounts received	90
Bank	5,245		
Balance c/d	3,065		
	29,350		29,350

Task 2

(a)   False

(b)   **(1)**   £46,380 **Note:** £77,300 x 0.6

        (2)   £12,050 **Note:** £10,500 + £47,930 - £46,380

        (3)   (a)   A high value item has not been included in the closing inventory figure

        (4)   £12,550

(c)   (a)   £4,400

(d)   (a)   It is unethical for an accounting technician to manipulate profit

Task 3

(a)   **Capital**

	£		£
Balance c/d	15,000	Bank	15,000
	15,000		15,000

(b)   (1)   £21,820

(2)   Tairo Trading
Statement of financial position as at 31 March 20-1

Non-current assets	Cost £	Accumulated depreciation £	Carrying amount £
Vehicles	35,300	10,250	25,050
Current assets			
Inventory		8,350	
Trade receivables		21,820	
Prepayments		330	
Total current assets		30,500	
Current liabilities			
Trade payables	10,260		
VAT	5,640		
Accruals	540		
Payroll liabilities	590		
Bank	1,270		
Total current liabilities		18,300	
Net current assets			12,200
Net assets			37,250
Financed by:			
Capital			
Opening capital			30,180
Add profit for the year			19,040
Less Drawings			11,970
Closing capital			37,250

(c)   On 1 April 20-1 capital account has an opening balance of **£37,250 credit**

Task 4

(a)   **(1)**   (d)   With more than one owner there is the possibility of increased capital for the partnership

(2)   A charity uses its resources to fund charitable activities under its control and is run by its **trustees**

(3)   (d)   All of them

(4)   The rules of an ordinary partnership are set out in either the **Partnership Act** or in a **written or oral** Partnership Agreement.

(b)   The International Financial Reporting Standard that sets out the format of final accounts for an organisation adopting IFRS is **IAS 1**.

(c)

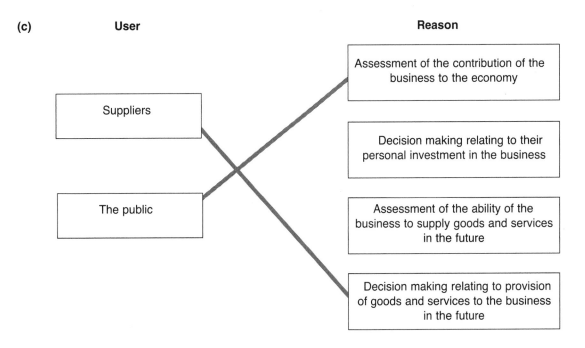

User	Reason
	Assessment of the contribution of the business to the economy
Suppliers	Decision making relating to their personal investment in the business
	Assessment of the ability of the business to supply goods and services in the future
The public	Decision making relating to provision of goods and services to the business in the future

Task 5

(a)

Statement	True	False
All partnership agreements state that profits and losses must be shared equally between the partners		✔
A partnership agreement states the salaries to be paid to employees		✔
A partnership agreement may state that interest is to be allowed on partners' capitals	✔	
A partnership agreement may state that interest is to be charged on partners' drawings	✔	

(b)   **Capital account – Kay**

	£		£
Loan	25,000	Balance b/d	48,500
Bank	35,500	Goodwill	12,000
	60,500		60,500

(c)   Partnership appropriation account for the year ended 31 December 20-1

	£
Profit for appropriation	68,000
Salary – Jane	–12,000
Salary – Kate	–18,000
Sales commission – Jane	–8,000
Sales commission – Kate	–6,000
Residual profit available for distribution	24,000
Share of residual profit or loss	
Share of profit or loss – Jane	14,400
Share of profit or loss – Kate	9,600
Total residual profit or loss distributed	24,000

The opening balance of Jane's partnership current account at 1 January 20-2 will be **£11,500 credit**

Task 6

(a)

Beacon Partnership Statement of profit or loss for the year ended 31 March 20-7		
	£	£
Sales revenue		165,230
Opening inventory	15,140	
Purchases	85,460	
Closing inventory	−17,380	
Cost of sales		83,220
Gross profit		82,010
Add:		
Disposal of non-current asset		520
Less:		
Administration expenses	20,830	
Allowance for doubtful debts adjustment	250	
Depreciation charges	4,650	
Loan interest paid	760	
Payroll expenses	30,980	
Selling expenses	6,340	
Total expenses		63,810
Profit/loss for the year		18,720

(b)

	£
Yulia – share of profit or loss	9,360
Yulia – final current account balance	8,410

     (b)   Within the 'Financed by' section

(c)   (b)   2 and 3

Answers to practice assessment 2

Task 1

(a) **Purchases ledger control account**

Discounts received	306	Balance b/d	12,600
Bank	102,145	Purchases day book	103,200
Balance c/d	13,349		
	115,800		115,800

(b) **VAT control account**

Purchases day book	17,200	Balance b/d	3,290
Administration expenses	4,060	Sales day book	30,800
Discounts allowed	80	Discounts received	51
Bank	8,680		
Balance c/d	4,121		
	34,141		34,141

(c) **Bank account**

Sales ledger control	183,110	Balance b/d	2,430
		Purchases ledger control	102,145
		HMRC for VAT	8,680
		Administration expenses	24,360
		Payroll expenses	25,490
		Drawings	16,300
		Balance c/d	3,705
	183,110		183,110

Task 2

(a)   True

(b)   **(1)**   £50,000 **Note:** £75,000 x 2/3

     (2)   £52,500 **Note:** £50,000 + £15,000 - £12,500

     (3)   (b) The trader has made drawings of goods during the year

     (4)   £14,250

(c)   **(a)**   £7,000

(d)   **(c)**   Ask for another manager to supervise your work

Task 3

(a)   **Capital**

	£		£
Bank	13,300	Balance b/d	35,600
Goods for own use	750	Profit for the year	16,900
Balance c/d	38,450		
	52,500		52,500

(b)   **(1)**   £32,390

(2)   **Dracus Trading**
Statement of financial position as at 31 March 20-1

Non-current assets	Cost £	Accumulated depreciation £	Carrying amount £
Office equipment	30,730	16,250	14,480
Current assets			
Inventory		18,190	
Trade receivables		32,390	
Prepayments		450	
Total current assets		51,030	
Current liabilities			
Trade payables	15,380		
VAT	6,840		
Accruals	240		
Payroll liabilities	550		
Bank	2,480		
Total current liabilities		25,490	
Net current assets			25,540
Net assets			40,020
Financed by:			
Capital			
Opening capital			39,460
Add Profit for the year			16,100
Less Drawings			15,540
Closing capital			40,020

(c)   On 1 April 20-1 capital account has an opening balance of **£40,020 credit**

Task 4

(a)   **(1)**   (a)   There is continuing existence of the business as a separate legal entity

(2)   A limited company is run by its **directors** on behalf of its **shareholders**

(3)   (a) 3 only

(4)   A charity uses its resources to fund **charitable** activities and is run by its **trustees** in accordance with the **Charities Act**

(b)   (d)   All of them

(c)   **User**   **Reason**

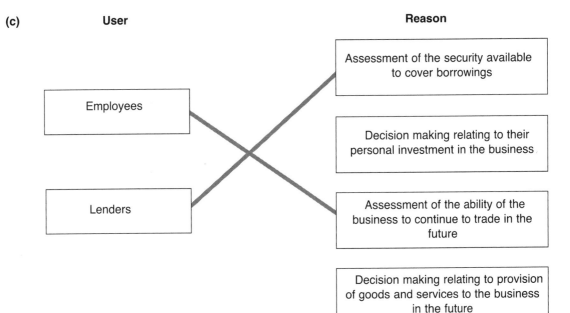

Task 5

(a)

Transaction	Capital account		Current account	
	Dr	Cr	Dr	Cr
Capital introduced		✔		
Partner's salary				✔
Drawings			✔	
Goodwill created		✔		
Share of losses			✔	
Interest on capital				✔

(b)   **Partners' capital accounts**

	Freya £	Gina £		Freya £	Gina £
Goodwill	12,000	18,000	Balances b/d	24,000	36,000
Balances c/d	27,000	33,000	Goodwill	15,000	15,000
	39,000	51,000		39,000	51,000

(c)   **Partnership appropriation account for the year ended 31 December 20-1**

	£
Profit for appropriation	33,000
Salary – Rob	−10,800
Salary – Sue	−13,800
Sales commission – Rob	−4,500
Sales commission – Sue	−5,750
Residual profit available for distribution	−1,850
Share of residual profit or loss	
Share of profit or loss – Rob	−740
Share of profit or loss – Sue	−1,110
Total residual profit or loss distributed	−1,850

The opening balance of Rob's partnership current account at 1 January 20-2 will be **£990 credit**

Task 6

(a)

Sarton Partnership		
Statement of profit or loss for the year ended 31 March 20-1		
	£	£
Sales revenue		95,320
Opening inventory	5,150	
Purchases	45,930	
Closing inventory	−6,090	
Cost of sales		44,990
Gross profit		50,330
Add:		
Disposal of non-current asset		160
Less:		
Administration expenses	16,210	
Allowance for doubtful debts adjustment	120	
Depreciation charges	4,750	
Loan interest paid	1,095	
Payroll expenses	24,975	
Selling expenses	12,410	
Total expenses		59,560
Profit/loss for the year		−9,070

(b)

	£
Sara – share of profit or loss	−5,442
Sara – final current account balance	2,822

(a)   Deducted within the 'Financed by' section

(c)

Item	Statement of profit or loss	Statement of financial position
Property, plant and equipment		✔
Tax expense	✔	
Finance costs	✔	
Share premium		✔

Answers to practice assessment 3

Task 1

(a) **Purchases ledger control account**

	£		£
Bank	27,846	Balance b/d	4,367
Balance c/d	4,498	Credit purchases	27,977
	32,344		32,344

(b) **Sales ledger control account**

Balance b/d	8,216	Bank	67,031
Credit sales	68,422	Irrecoverable debts	560
		Balance c/d	9,047
	76,638		76,638

(c) **Bank account**

Sales ledger control	67,031	Balance b/d	3,219
		Purchases ledger control	27,846
		Drawings	12,500
		Office expenses	19,361
		Bank interest paid	247
		Cash purchases	2,612
		Balance c/d	1,246
	67,031		67,031

Task 2

(a)   False

(b)   **(1)**   £64,000 **Note:** £80,000 x 4/5

      (2)   £67,000 **Note:** £64,000 + £10,000 – £7,000

      (3)   (d)   Some sales returns items have been included twice in the count

      (4)   £9,800

(c)   (b)   £9,300

(d)   (b)   The financial statements prepared by the accountant do not contain false or misleading figures and statements

Task 3

(a)   **Capital**

	£		£
Balance c/d	23,500	Bank	20,000
		Purchases	3,500
	23,500		23,500

(b) **(1)** **£123,700** ie £125,860 − £2,160

(2) **£49,290** ie £47,860 + £1,430

(3)

Hanslo Trading
Statement of profit or loss for the year ended 31 March 20-6

	£	£
Sales revenue		123,700
Opening inventory	9,760	
Purchases	49,290	
Closing inventory	−11,340	
Cost of sales		47,710
Gross profit		75,990
Add:		
Disposal of non-current assets		990
Less:		
Carriage outwards	2,790	
Depreciation charges	4,520	
General expenses	23,920	
Payroll expenses	49,050	
Total expenses		80,280
Profit/loss for the year		−3,300

(c) The business has made a loss on disposal

Task 4

(a) **(1)** (d) When information contained in the financial statements is untrue and could influence the economic decisions of users

(2) The governing document of a charity is the **Trust Deed**

(3) (c) 2 and 3

(4) A company incorporates by registering under **the Companies Act**

Once registered, a company is run by its **directors**

(b) (a) Relevance

(d) Faithful representation

(c)

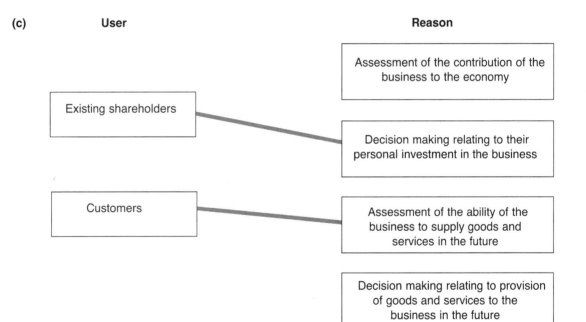

User		Reason
		Assessment of the contribution of the business to the economy
Existing shareholders		Decision making relating to their personal investment in the business
Customers		Assessment of the ability of the business to supply goods and services in the future
		Decision making relating to provision of goods and services to the business in the future

Task 5

(a)

Statement	True	False
When a new partner is admitted to a partnership business, existing partners pay a premium to welcome the new partner		✔
When a partner retires from a partnership business, the balance of his or her capital and current accounts is due to the partner from the partnership	✔	
Goodwill is kept in a separate bank account in accordance with the requirements of the Partnership Act 1890		✔

(b)   (1)

Account name	Amount £	Debit	Credit
Goodwill	60,000		✔
Capital – Hal	36,000	✔	
Capital – Ian	24,000	✔	

(2)   Hal's share of the profits and losses in the partnership has **decreased** after the change in the partnership agreement.

Hal's capital account balance has **increased** after the change in the partnership agreement.

Final Accounts Preparation

Workbook

David Cox

Published by Osborne Books Limited
Tel 01905 748071
Email books@osbornebooks.co.uk
Website www.osbornebooks.co.uk

Design by Laura Ingham

Printed by CPI Group (UK) Limited, Croydon, CR0 4YY, on environmentally friendly, acid-free paper from managed forests.

MIX
Paper from
responsible sources
FSC® C019777

British Library Cataloguing in Publication Data
A catalogue record for this book is available from the British Library

ISBN 978 1909173 804